This book is about
A DOG
called

Faithful Friend

THE DOG RECORD BOOK

Contents

From the Start

What is your dog's name?
....

Why did you choose this name?
....

....

....

Does your dog have a nickname?
....

When was your dog born?
....

What gender is it?
....

Photograph

From the Start

What breed is it? Is your dog typical of the breed?
....
....
....
....
....

How would you describe the type and colour of its coat?
....
....
....
....
....

Does it have any special markings?
....
....
....

What colour are its eyes?
....
....
....

Do you know the details of your dog's parents?

FATHER	MOTHER
Name	Name
Breed	Breed
Colour	Colour

From the Start

How many puppies were there in the litter?

Do you know how many brothers and how many sisters your dog has?

Did you have a number of puppies to choose from? Why did you choose this particular one?

Where did you get your dog from?

Name:

Address:

Phone number:

Puppy Days

How old was your puppy when you brought it home?

....

....

....

What does it look like? What sort of character does it have? Does it have any unusual

features or habits?

....

....

....

....

What sort of bark does your puppy have? How does your puppy behave when happy?

....

....

....

When does your puppy have its meals? What food and drink do you normally give it?

....

....

....

Does it like any unusual foods? Does it need any special care?

....

....

....

....

....

Puppy Days

What does your puppy like to chew? Has it ever damaged any furniture?

What special memories do you have of your puppy?

*Buy a pup and your
money will buy love unflinching.*
RUDYARD KIPLING

Housetraining

How long did it take to housetrain your dog?

....

....

....

....

....

Were there any unfortunate accidents?

....

....

....

....

....

Does your dog use a dog flap?

....

....

....

If so, how long did it take to learn to use it?

....

....

....

....

....

....

....

Lead and Collar

What type of collar does your dog have?

....

....

....

Does it carry an identity disc? If so, what are the details on the disc?

....

....

....

....

....

....

....

What type of lead/halter does your dog use? Does it like walking on the lead?

....

....

....

....

....

....

Is your dog able to walk at your command off the lead?

....

....

....

....

....

Learning to Obey

Has your dog ever attended training classes? If so, for how long, where and when?

....

....

Instructor's name:
....

Which of the following basic commands has your dog learned, and when?

'Come'	Date:
'Sit'	Date:
'Stay'	Date:
'Down'	Date:
'Heel'	Date:
'Fetch'	Date:
'Stand'	Date:
'Bed'	Date:

Have you taught your dog any special tricks?

....

....

....

....

....

Learning to Obey

Is it well behaved?

....

....

....

....

....

....

....

*Most dog owners are at length able
to teach themselves to obey their dog.*
ROBERT MORLEY

Character

What sort of personality and temperament does your dog have?

....

....

....

....

Is it very independent?

....

....

....

Is it affectionate? How does it show its affection?

....

....

....

....

The most affectionate creature
in the world is a wet dog.
AMBROSE BIERCE

Character

> Photograph

Is your dog easily frightened? By anything in particular?

What are its distinguishing traits? Are these typical of the breed?

Does it have a good sense of smell?

Sleeping

What type of bed or basket did your dog have as a puppy?

....

....

....

....

....

Where was it placed?

....

....

....

What bedding did your puppy like?

....

....

....

....

....

....

....

....

....

Sleeping

What type of bed or basket does your dog have now?

Where is it?

What bedding does your dog like now?

Where are its other favourite sleeping places?

Favourite Foods

How many times a day do you feed your dog? At what times?

....

....

How much food do you normally give at each meal?

....

....

Is your dog fussy about food? Does it need a special diet?

....

....

....

FAVOURITE FOODS

MAIN MEAL

....

....

....

MAIN MEAL

....

....

....

MAIN MEAL

....

....

....

Favourite Foods

Man is an animal that makes bargains;
no other animal does this – no dog exchanges bones with another.
ADAM SMITH

Do you ever give it bones?

What treats do you give your dog? Do you give it any special food on its birthday?

What does it usually drink?

Play/Toys

As a puppy, what were its favourite toys?

....

....

....

....

What are its favourite playthings now?

....

....

....

What games does your dog like to play?

....

....

....

....

Does your dog like playing in water? Is it a good swimmer?

....

....

....

Does your dog watch television? Does it have a favourite programme?

....

....

....

....

Play/Toys

Does your dog like music? What sort? Does it ever 'sing'?

....

....

....

....

Does your dog take anything to bed with it?

....

....

....

....

Photograph

In the Garden

Does your dog have an outdoor kennel?

Is your dog allowed in the garden? Does it tend to dig things up?

Has it ever got through into a neighbour's garden?

In the Garden

Has it ever run away?

How long for?

How territorial is your dog?

*Dogs laugh,
but they laugh with their tails.*
MAX EASTMAN

Has your dog ever bitten the postman? Or anyone else?

Favourite Walks

How much exercise do you give your dog each day?

....

....

....

At what times of day?

....

....

....

Who loves me will love my dog also.
ST BERNARD

Favourite Walks

WALK 1

Route:
....
....

Length:
....

Time:
....

Favourite spot:
....
....

WALK 2

Route:
....
....
....
....

Length:
....

Time:
....

Favourite spot:
....
....
....
....
....

Favourite Walks

WALK 3

Route:
....
....

Length:
....

Time:
....

Favourite spot:
....
....

WALK 4

Route:
....
....

Length:
....

Time:
....

Favourite spot:
....
....

WALK 5

Route:
....
....

Length:
....

Time:
....

Favourite spot:
....
....

Favourite Walks

WALK 6

Route:
....
....
....

Length:
....

Time:
....

Favourite spot:
....
....

No man is so poor that he can't afford to keep one dog,
and I've seen them so poor that they could afford to keep three.
JOSH BILLINGS

Other Dogs and Other Animals

How does your dog behave with other dogs? Does it behave differently with dogs of different breeds and sizes?

Do you have any other dogs yourself?

What other dogs have you had in the past?

Other Dogs and Other Animals

Does your dog have any special doggie friends?

Has it ever been in a serious fight?

Is your dog friendly with animals other than dogs? Does it chase cats? Birds?

Favourite People

Which of your friends are firm favourites of your dog?

Is your dog sociable and welcoming?

Would you say your dog is a good companion?

How does it behave with children?

Dogs are evidently intended by God to be our companions,
protectors and, in many ways, examples.
FATHER BERTRAND WILBERFORCE

Clean and Tidy

With what frequency do you groom your dog?

What type of brush/comb do you use?

How often do you give your dog a bath?

How frequently do its claws need clipping?

Clean and Tidy

Do you use any anti-flea treatment on your dog? What sort, and how often?

Does your dog ever have its teeth cleaned?

What about its ears?

Earning a Living

Is your dog a working dog or guard dog? If so, what special attributes are needed?

Has it undergone any advanced training?

Earning a Living

Has it ever performed a heroic deed?

Photograph

Adventures

What is the greatest adventure your dog has ever had?

....
....
....
....
....

Has it ever gone missing? Under what circumstances and for how long?

....
....
....
....
....
....

Has your dog ever been on a walk and found something really exciting? What was it?

....
....
....
....
....

Adventures

The dog is man's best friend,
He has a tail on one end,
Up in front he has teeth,
And four legs underneath.
OGDEN NASH

Has your dog ever become too tired to want to walk home? What did you do?

Holidays

Has your dog ever gone away with you on holiday? If so, where did you go and with whom?

Date:

Place:

With:

Date:

Place:

With:

Date:

Place:

With:

How did you travel?

Does it enjoy going away?

Holidays

Do you ever use boarding kennels?

....

....

Which kennels do you prefer to use?

Name:

....

Address:

....

....

....

Phone number:

....

Cost per day:

....

Has your dog ever had to spend time in quarantine? If so, when and where?

....

....

....

....

....

....

....

....

....

....

....

....

Parenthood

Has your dog ever had puppies?

Two dogs were talking.
"What's your name?"
asked the first.
"I'm not sure,"
replied the second,
"but I think it must be
'Down Boy!'"

Parenthood

What was the mate's breed, colouring and markings?

Parenthood

When was the litter born? How many were in the litter?

....

....

NAMES	COLOUR/MARKINGS	SEX

Photograph

Parenthood

Do you have any memories of them being weaned and reared?

....

....

....

....

....

....

....

....

....

....

....

....

....

....

....

....

What new homes did the puppies go to?

....

NAME of puppy	NAME & ADDRESS of new owner

Showing Off

Have you ever entered your dog for shows? What was the first

occasion?

Does your dog like going to shows? Does it behave differently when on show? Has it ever

misbehaved?

What is the most important show your dog has entered?

Has it won any prizes? If so, at which show, and where was it placed?

SHOW/CLASS	DATE	RESULTS/PRIZES

Showing Off

Do you have any show
ambitions for your dog?

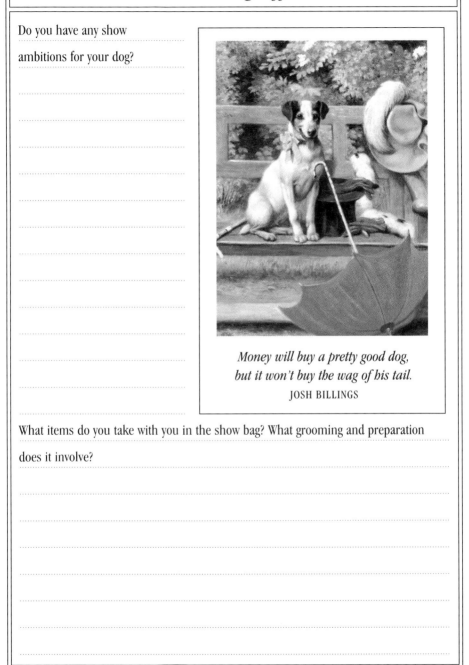

Money will buy a pretty good dog,
but it won't buy the wag of his tail.
JOSH BILLINGS

What items do you take with you in the show bag? What grooming and preparation
does it involve?

Medical Record

What is the veterinary surgeon's name?

....

....

....

Name of practice:

....

Address:

....

....

....

Phone number:

....

What are the surgery hours?

....

....

....

List below the vaccinations which have been given to your dog and when.

COMBINED VACCINATIONS AGAINST		
Canine distemper, Canine hepatitis, and Canine parvovirus		
Age of Puppy	Date Given	Cost
8 weeks		
12 weeks		
16 weeks		
Age of Dog	Booster Dates	Cost

Medical Record

Use the next two pages to compile the medical history of your dog.

WORMING TABLETS		KENNEL COUGH NASAL VACCINE	
Date Given	Cost	Date Given	Cost

ILLNESSES/AILMENTS

Illness	Date	Cost

Medical Record

CHECK-UPS AND OTHER VISITS

Reason for Visit	Date	Cost

OPERATIONS

Type of Operation	Date	Cost

A dog is loved by old and young.
He wags his tail, and not his tongue.
FALMER'S ALMANAC

Insurance

Do you have any medical insurance for your dog?

Which company is the insurance with?

Address:

Phone number:

Policy number:

Premium renewal date:

Annual premium:

CLAIMS	DATE	SETTLED

ALSO IN THIS SERIES
Nine Lives – THE CAT RECORD BOOK

FOUR SEASONS
PUBLISHING LIMITED

Published in England by
FOUR SEASONS PUBLISHING LTD.
16 Orchard Rise, Kingston Upon Thames, KT2 7EY, England

Designed and typeset by Judith Pedersen
Printed in India

ISBN 1 85645 134 8

ACKNOWLEDGEMENTS
Four Seasons Publishing Ltd would like to thank all those who kindly gave permission to reproduce the words and visual material in this book; copyright holders have been identified where possible and we apologise for any inadvertent omissions.

Front Cover: *A Black and Tan Collie* ROBERT MORLEY
Back Cover and page 7: *A Collie with Fox Terrier Puppies* WALTER HUNT
Title Page: *Yorkie* JOHN EMMS
Page 11: *A Portrait of Nettle, a Terrier* JOHN EMMS
Page 12: *Irish Wolf Hounds* SIR EDWIN HENRY LANDSEER
Page 17: *Doubtful Crumbs* SIR EDWIN HENRY LANDSEER
Page 21: *Intrigue* JULIUS ADAM
Pages 22/23: *Pointers* EUGENE PETIT
Page 25: *Live and Let Live* BASIL BRADLEY
Page 29: *Susan on a Balcony* MARY CASSATT
Page 35: *"Brownie" and "Shultze"* JOHN EMMS
Pages 38/39: *Proud of her Litter* JOHN SARGENT NOBLE
Page 43: *Where are They?* WILLIAM WEEKES
Page 47: *Young Girl with a Dog* PIERRE AUGUSTE RENOIR

All images supplied by Fine Art Photographic Library Ltd., with the exception of those on the Front and Back Covers and pages 7, 17, 25, 29, 43 and 47, which were supplied by The Bridgeman Art Library/Visual Arts Library.